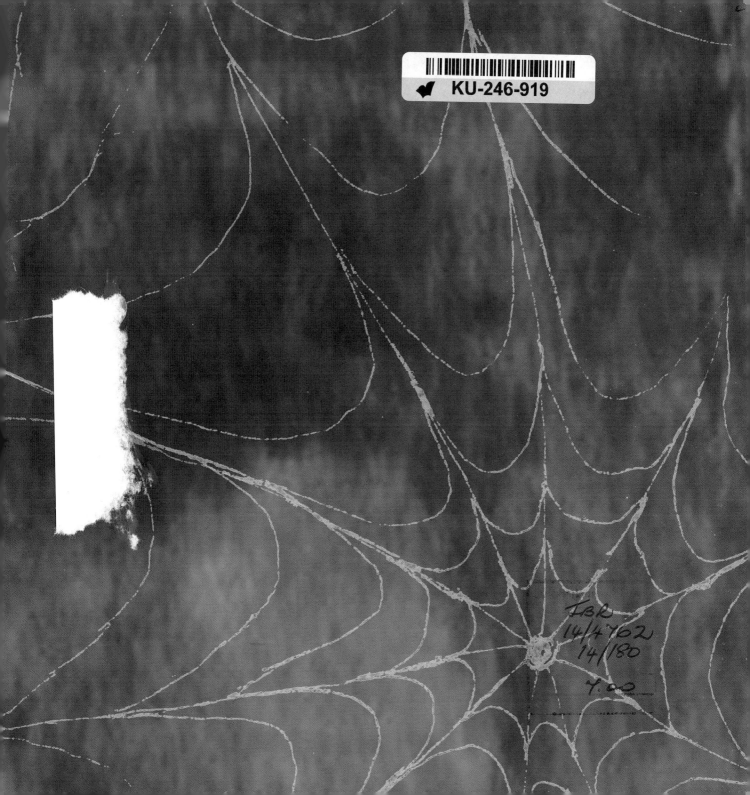

TBR
14/4702
14/180

4.00

To all who are afraid of spiders

Published by Dbee Press
8 New Row, Mullingar, Co. Westmeath, Ireland
Text copyright © Dolores Keaveney 2014
Illustration copyright © Dolores Keaveney 2014
Artwork copyright © Dolores Keaveney 2014

Printed in Ireland by KPS Colour Print Ltd
Design & Layout by Gary Kelly

Written and Illustrated by Dolores Keaveney
www.doloreskeaveney.com

ISBN 9780957191754

The Scary Spider

written and illustrated
by Dolores Keaveney

There was a
Scary Spider,
the biggest
I ever did see,
sitting on my
window sill
just staring
right at Me,

I shushed and hushed,
and hushed and shushed,
to frighten her away,
but the Scary Spider
sat there
and decided
she would stay.

She wove a web
of silver thread,
so big it filled
my window sill,

and sat in wait
to catch her tea,
sitting there
so calm and still

Up came a fly
just buzzing by,
and never saw
the silver thread,

And in it flew
to the silver trap,
which clung so tightly
to its head.

The Scary Spider scrambled down, to devour her latest prey,

but just before
this happened,

the big fly
flew away.

The spider swung
from right to left,

up overhead
and down,

along her silver
web so strong,
as I watched her
with a frown.

I'll gather up some food,
I thought,
and feed her just today,
some buns, some bread
and biscuits
I found without delay.

I ran up to the window sill
to leave my little treat,
the spider would be happy
to have something nice to eat.

There was no
Scary Spider,
sitting on my window sill,
no silver web
made of silver thread
hanging very still.

Maybe tomorrow, or next week,

I'll wait right here 'til then.

If you liked this
book, you'll love...

If I were
a bee
I'd dance on a Sunflower...
Written & Illustrated by Dolores Keaveney

Jenny
the little
brown hen
ny
rc
dhonn
Written & Illustrated by Dolores Keaveney
will never be
lonely again...
sásta anois
lena clann ...

The Adventures of Jenny,
Sylvester..
...and their
Six Little Chicks

Beelicious
Recipes with Honey

First cookery book for boys & girls

Illustrated & compiled by Dolores Keaveney

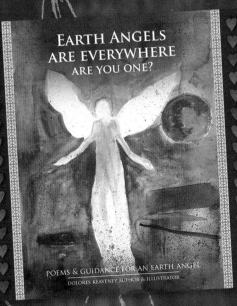

EARTH ANGELS
ARE EVERYWHERE
ARE YOU ONE?

POEMS & GUIDANCE FOR AN EARTH ANGEL
DOLORES KEAVENEY AUTHOR & ILLUSTRATOR

Meet the
fairies
in my
backyard

Written and Illustrated by Dolores Keaveney

Available in book
stores nationwide
and online at
www.doloreskeaveney.com

it the
ary Spider
sat there

decided

About the Author

I am an artist and have been painting for the best part of 40 years. My art is vibrant, colourful, loose and uplifting. I get my inspiration from my garden when in summertime it is packed full of beautiful flowers. I am also a self published author/illustrator of children's picture books. In 2009 I launched my first picture book 'If I were a bee'… This book was a great success for me and spurred me on to write and illustrate more. So I have continued to launch one or two books per year since then.

If you would like to see my children's picture books, please visit doloreskeaveney.com